The New Bug in Town

Brandi Smeltzer

Illustrations by
Emily Zieroth

Green Meadow Publishing

Text and Illustrations copyright © 2022 Brandi Smeltzer
Published by Green Meadow Publishing
Freedom, IN

Cover design and illustrations by Emily Zieroth

Hardcover ISBN: 978-1-7345738-2-4
Paperback ISBN: 978-1-7345738-3-1

Library of Congress Control Number: 2022902816
Smeltzer, Brandi

The New Bug in Town / Brandi Smeltzer
Life was comfortable in Larvadale…until the new bug moved to town.

ISBN: 978-1-7345738-2-4

The New Bug in Town

Brandi Smeltzer

Illustrations by Emily Zieroth

Larvadale was a sleepy town. Nothing exciting ever happened. Each insect did its own work and minded its own business.

The citizens of Larvadale could not even remember the last time a predator had charged into town, terrorizing the village in search of its next meal.

The next day, the new bug-now nicknamed Cow Killer-started off on a stroll through her new town.

The pill bugs didn't answer. Instead, they sped off toward a taxi.

She walked on until she found three beautiful butterflies sipping hot cups of brew outside the local nectar shop.

Then she heard a loud commotion outside. Footsteps pounded the sidewalk. Screams of terror rang in her ears.

She ran to the window.

The citizens were running for their lives as a giant monster chased them down the street!

She dashed out her front door and into the street, throwing herself between the bird and the citizens of Larvadale.

The animal's big, black eyes zeroed in on her as it came close, opening its beak.

The crowd gasped! The bird halted! None had ever seen a stinger so massive.

The bird squawked and flew away, leaving Cow Killer alone in the street, facing the crowd. There was silence as every bug in Larvadale stared at her.

Of course
I can!

The crowd cheered
once more. Velvet
finally felt at home.

From that day on, all
new bugs were
welcome in Larvadale.

What to Do If You Spot a Velvet Ant

Cow Killer, also known by her scientific name Dasymutilla occidentalis, inhabits the United States as far west as Texas. She is most commonly seen in clover fields, meadows, and forest edges. She may even be in your own back yard!

This velvet ant is not an enemy, but she is also not a companion-so it is best not to capture her. If confronted by a human, she will run very fast to get away. Let her! If she feels threatened, she will fight fiercely and try to sting, and her sting is so powerful that many believe it can kill a cow! This false assumption has earned her the nickname Cow Killer. Trying to stomp or squash her is futile; her exoskeleton is unusually strong, making her nearly impossible to kill. Because of her super-insect speed, strength, and sting, experts say it is best to admire her from a safe, respectable distance.

Fun Facts

- Named the velvet ant because of her hairy, ant-shaped body, this insect is actually a wingless female wasp.
- Cow Killer is a real nickname for the velvet ant you saw in this story.
- Cow Killer invades underground bumblebee burrows and lays her eggs on the bee's nesting larvae. When the eggs hatch, the velvet ant larvae eat the surrounding bumblebee larvae. This helps keep the bumblebee population from getting out of control.
- Adult velvet ants feed on nectar and water.
- Cow Killer must crawl through tight spaces to lay her eggs, and wings would only get in her way. Male wasps do not lay eggs, so they get to do all the flying.
- Because males have wings and do not sting, many scientist have mistaken the male and female as two different species.
- The velvet ant's bright coloration is a warning to predators. Additionally, both male and female deliver a squeaking noise by rubbing a special organ in their abdomen to scare away enemies.
- Cow Killer has an exoskeleton so strong that it is almost impossible to destroy.
- There are approximately 3000 known species of velvet ants throughout the world.

About the Author

Brandi Smeltzer is a former middle school language arts teacher who left public education to homeschool her three children. She enjoys reading, writing, and spending quality time with her family. Brandi lives in Indiana with her husband and three children. For more information, visit http://www.BrandiSmeltzer.com

About the Illustrator

Emily Zieroth is a Canadian, self-taught artist who has been illustrating children's books for over a decade. It has become her true passion, and the thought that kids from around the world smile at the illustrations she has drawn brings such joy to her life. With every book comes a new adventure and a new chance to learn and grow. She hopes that she is able to portray her love for her work with every story she illustrates.

Other Books by Brandi Smeltzer

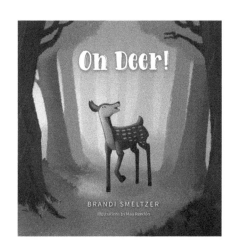

As a thunderstorm looms in the distance, Brooklyn spots a fawn in trouble. Brooklyn must decide whether to intervene or allow nature to run its course.

Read to see what happens to the young deer in this incredible true story and also learn some fun facts about fawns, including what to do if you spot one alone.

Available on Amazon and online wherever books are sold.

Lightning Source UK Ltd.
Milton Keynes UK
UKHW052202070422
401237UK00002B/45